For Tara
with love

V.F.

First published 1991 by Walker Books Ltd
87 Vauxhall Walk, London SE11 5HJ

This edition published 2002

2 4 6 8 10 9 7 5 3 1

Text © 1991 Vivian French Illustrations © 1991 Jan Ormerod

This book has been typeset in Garamond

Printed in Hong Kong

British Library Cataloguing in Publication Data:
a catalogue record for this book is available from the British Library

ISBN 0-7445-8962-2

One Ballerina Two

Vivian French illustrated by Jan Ormerod

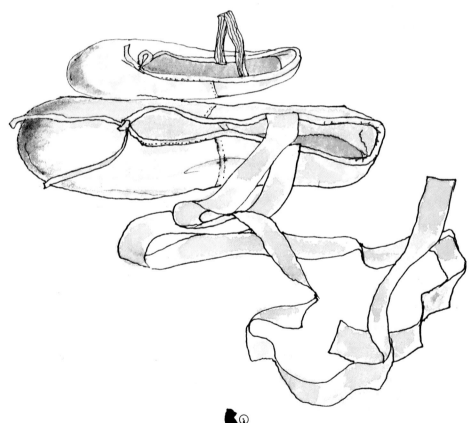

WALKER BOOKS

AND SUBSIDIARIES

LONDON • BOSTON • SYDNEY

Ballerinas…

us two

10 Ten pliés

9 Nine knee bends

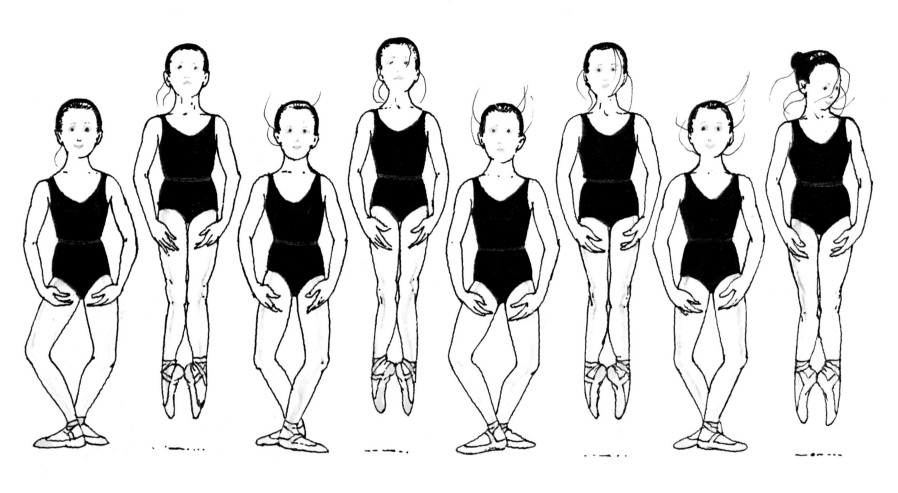

8 Eight changements

7 Seven little jumps

6 Six pirouettes

5 Five gallops

Oops!

4 Four pas de chat

3 Three pony trots

2 Two final curtsies

One happy hug

VIVIAN FRENCH says that she was inspired to write **One Ballerina Two** by Jan Ormerod's two daughters, who both learned ballet. "Jan did some rough sketches of them dancing," says Vivian, "and I liked them so much I was inspired to write this book!"

Vivian French worked in children's theatre for ten years as both an actor and writer before becoming an acclaimed children's author. Her picture books include *A Song for Little Toad* (shortlisted for the 1995 Smarties Book Prize), *Once Upon a Time*, *To Mum With Love* and the non-fiction titles *Caterpillar Caterpillar* (shortlisted for the Kurt Maschler Award) and *Growing Frogs*. She has also written many fiction titles for young readers. Vivian lives in Bristol.

JAN ORMEROD says of *One Ballerina Two*, "The characters are based upon my two dancing daughters – the little one adoring, scruffy and ungainly in her attempts to imitate the elegant, trained movements of her older sister."

Jan Ormerod won several major awards for her first book, *Sunshine*. She has since written and illustrated many books for children, including the Walker titles *Happy Christmas Gemma*, which was shortlisted for the Smarties Prize; *Eat Up, Gemma*, its follow up; and *Jump!* Jan was born and brought up in Western Australia but now lives in Cambridge, England.